# Written and Illustrated by Me!

Name_____

Age _____

Grade _____

Teacher _____

# Memories of a Weird Year!

## A Journal of My Life During the Coronavirus Pandemic

By Lauren Liss Bogart

Dear Friend,

This past year has been very strange. A disease called coronavirus or COVID-19 swept across the world and affected nearly everyone's life. An illness that makes people sick in many countries is called a pandemic. The coronavirus pandemic caused many things to be closed or canceled like schools, movie theaters, after-school sports and activities, vacations, and camps. A lot of schools switched to online learning. Some kids couldn't see their grandparents because they were afraid of getting them sick. People stayed in their houses more than usual and wore masks so they didn't catch or spread germs.

There are things about this year you will never forget, even many years from now when you are an adult. This journal will help you remember how your life changed during the coronavirus pandemic. This is your book — draw pictures or write about your memories. Share your journal with your family or teacher.

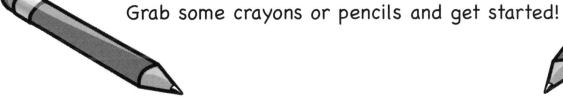

Grab some crayons or pencils and get started!

Sometimes we couldn't see our friends or family members during the pandemic. Birthday parties or field trips may have been canceled.

Draw or write about the activities and people you missed most.

Lots of people tried new activities so they weren't bored when they had to stay at home.

What are some new things you started doing?

Many times stores ran out of things we wanted.

What are some items your family had trouble finding?

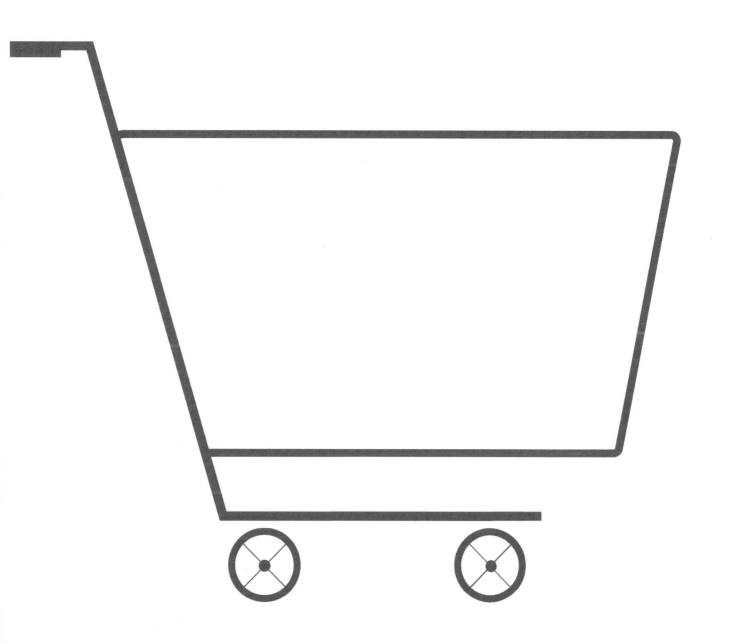

When you were spending a lot of time at home, you may have had many different feelings.

Circle or color the ones you felt.

| Scared | Happy | Nervous |
|--------|-------|---------|
| Confused | Sad | Free |
| Relaxed | Calm | Mad |
| Stressed | Bored | Relieved |

To help prevent the spread of germs, people started wearing masks.

Draw a picture of yourself wearing your favorite mask.

Everyone in your family was probably affected by the virus. Many parents started working from home while others stopped working. If you have brothers or sisters, they may have missed out on some fun activities or found new things to do just like you.

Draw pictures or write about your family members during the pandemic.

A lot of families started doing things together like taking walks, playing games, doing arts and crafts or baking together.

What have you enjoyed doing with your family?

There are times when adults are too busy to play or hang out.

What do you do to entertain yourself when you're alone?

● ● ● ● ● ● ● ● ● ● ● ● ● ● ● ● ● ● ● ● ● ● ● ● ● ● ● ● ● ● ● ● ● ● ● ● ●

Birthdays and holidays are usually shared with friends and family. This year may have been different.

How did you celebrate during the pandemic?

School changed a lot during the pandemic. Many children had to attend school online.

Draw a picture of your classroom <u>before</u> schools shut down.

What does going to school look like now?

The virus is mysterious to adults and children.
Even doctors and scientists don't have all the answers yet.
What are some questions you have about COVID-19?

_____

_____

_____

_____

_____

_____

_____

We all hope that the coronavirus germs go away soon
and stop making people sick.

What are you excited to do again when things get back to normal?

What's the best thing about this year you always hope to remember?

What was the hardest thing about this year you'll never forget?

More memories...

Parent recollections...

Share pictures of your child's journal pages on Instagram!

Tag us @kidsweirdyear or use #kidsweirdyear.

Made in the USA
Middletown, DE
24 December 2020